Making Connections®

Reading Comprehension Skills and Strategies

Book 2

EDUCATORS PUBLISHING SERVICE
Cambridge and Toronto

Contents

Unit 1: Identifying Detail

Unit 2: Sequencing

Unit 3: Main Idea

Unit 4: Compare and Contrast

Unit 5: Drawing Conclusions/Predicting Outcomes

Unit 6: Fact and Opinion

Unit 1

Identifying Detail Identifying detail is finding the words that describe something.

Popping Beans

What do nuña beans look like after they have been popped?

Many people love popcorn. But have you ever heard of popping beans? Popping beans, called nuña (say **noon**-yuh) beans, are found in the South American countries of Colombia, Ecuador, Peru, and Bolivia.

This map of South America shows Colombia, Ecuador, Peru, and Bolivia.

Nuña beans are fun to cook. They are fried in oil for a short time, until they suddenly pop open! The beans are then ready to eat as a healthy snack. Some people think they taste like peanuts.

Nuña beans are also interesting to look at. They can be very colorful, and sometimes they have spots. After they pop, they look like small butterflies with wide-open wings.

Nuña beans are a fun and different type of snack food. Would you like to eat a nuña bean?

Nuña beans come in many different colors.

Practice the Skill

Identify Details

1. Write three details about what nuña beans look like.

- look like eggs
- Have stripes
- Butterflies

2. Write two details about cooking nuña beans.

- fried in OIL
- fun to cook

Think and Draw

1. Draw a nuña bean after it has popped.

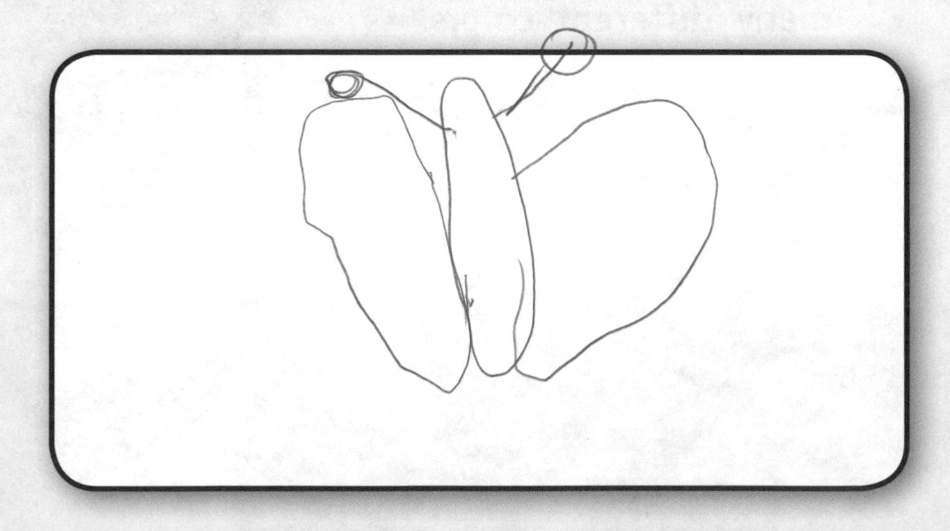

2. Make up another name for nuña beans that describes how popped beans look.

butterfly beans

Check Comprehension

1. List four countries where nuña beans are found.

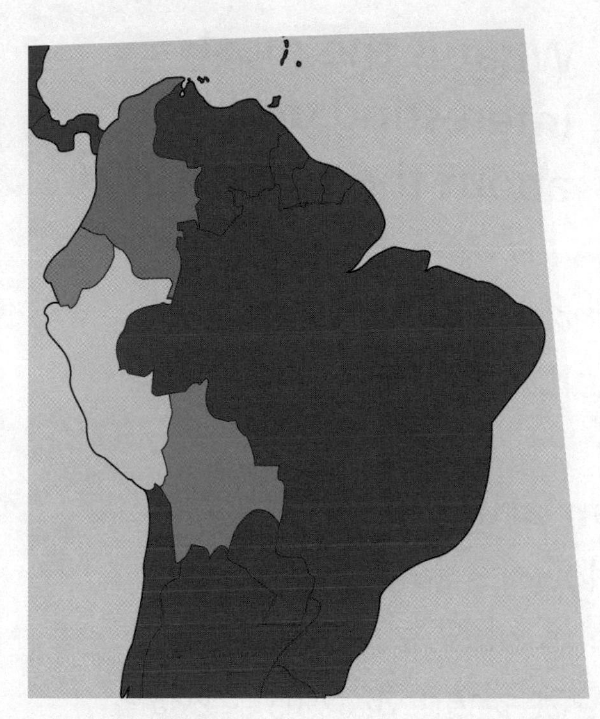

- colombia
- Peru
- Ecquador
- Bolivia

2. What makes nuña beans pop?

hot oil

3. What do nuña beans taste like?

Peanuts

Writing

& and

Write about your favorite snack. Write what it looks like and what it tastes like.

I like PB&J. It tastes sweet!

Titan Arum Trip

What is the most interesting detail about the titan arum?

Monday

Tomorrow my class is going to the botanical gardens. We are going to visit a special kind of flower called a titan arum.

My teacher said the titan arum is very rare and is one of the largest flowers in the world. It lives for forty years, but it only blooms two or three times in its life. And then it only stays open for two days!

My teacher told us to bring a handkerchief or tissue. When I asked why, she just smiled and said we'd find out.

A titan arum flower

Tuesday

Wow! The titan arum was enormous! It looked like an upside-down bell. It was green on the outside and red on the inside. I thought I was looking at one flower, but it was really thousands of tiny flowers. It had a tall part sticking out called a spadix. The spadix was over six feet tall!

I was so glad I had my handkerchief to put over my nose because the flower *stank!* The smell was like rotten meat. Insects such as beetles and bees may like the smell, but we didn't!

Our teacher took a picture of us.

Practice the Skill

Identify Details

Fill in the details about the titan arum.

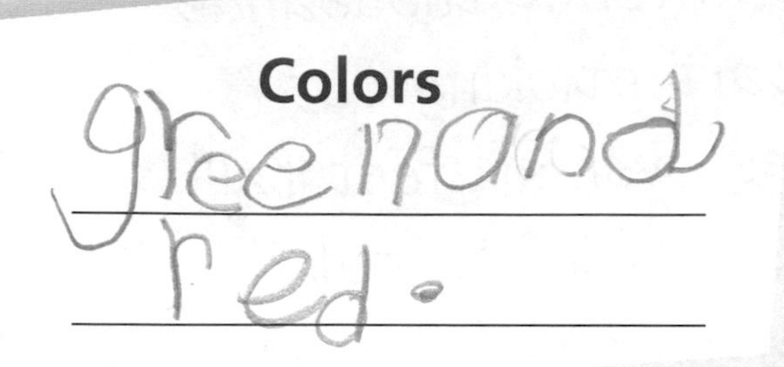

Smell

rotin meat

Lifespan

forty

True or False

Write "T" for true or "F" for false in each box.

- The titan arum is very rare. T
- It is the smallest flower in the world. F
- It blooms every day. F
- The titan arum stays open for two days. T
- Beetles and bees like the smell. T
- The flower stinks. T

Check Comprehension

1. Why did the writer need a tissue or handkerchief?

2. Is the plant's spadix taller or shorter than you?

Vocabulary

Find a word on page 9 that means "very big."

enormous

Venus Flytrap

How do Venus flytraps catch bugs and flies?

Venus flytrap is my name,
I'm very glad to meet you.
If you are a bug or fly,
Come closer and I'll eat you!

My leaves are green; my blooms are white;
I grow in Carolina.
My traps are colored green and red,
You'll never see them finer.

I can grow in a flowerpot,
Filled up with sand and peat.
I like my water fresh and clean,
But please don't drown my feet.

I want the sun to shine on me,
It helps to keep me happy.
But if I'm getting hungry, then
My traps get very snappy!

Insects like to sit on me,
A fly or tasty bug.
My traps will close around it,
And keep it nice and snug.

Venus flytrap is my name,
It's been so nice to meet you.
Come in closer, little fly,
Now I'm going to eat you!

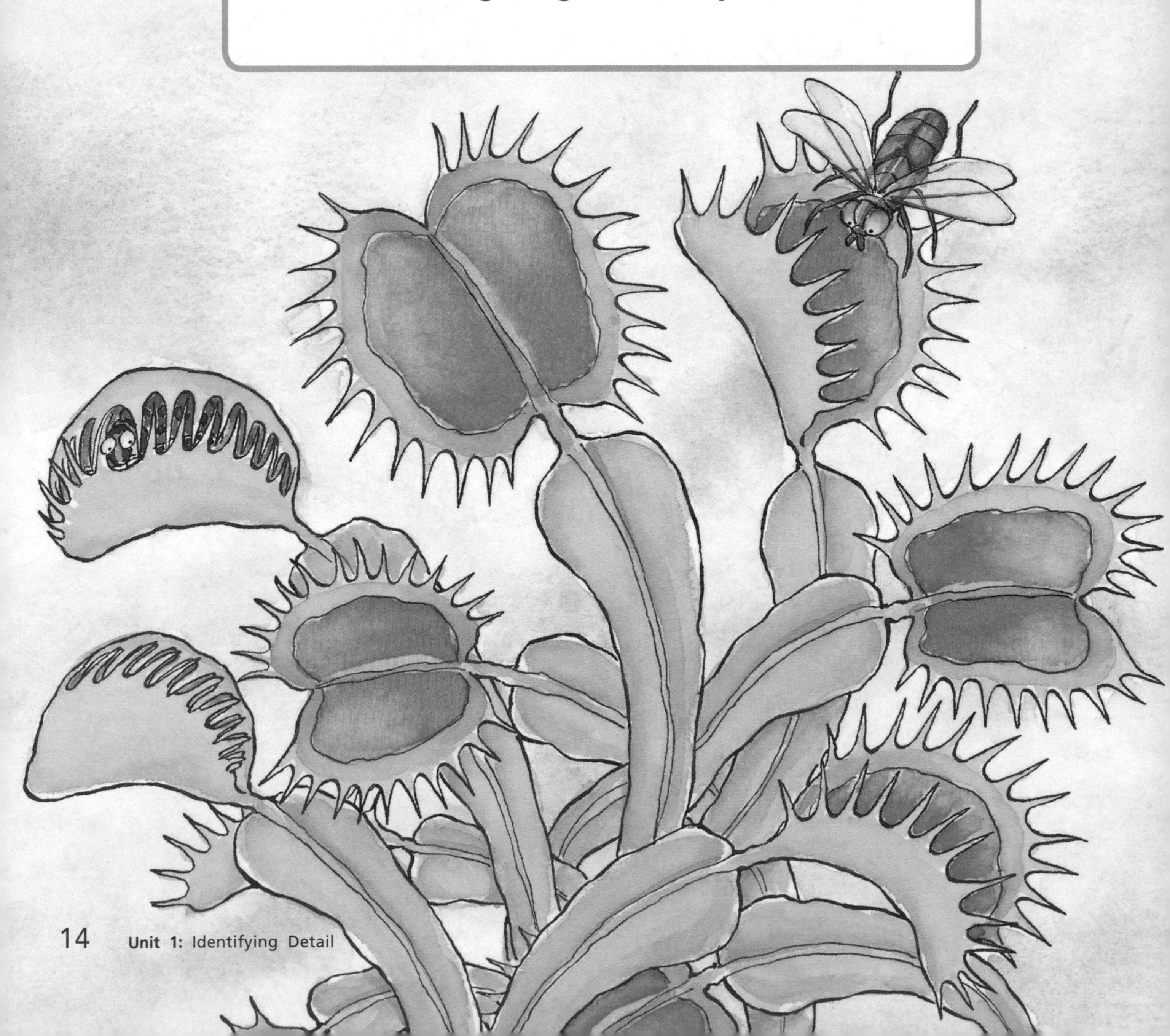

Practice the Skill

Identify Plant Details

What color is each part of the plant? Label it.

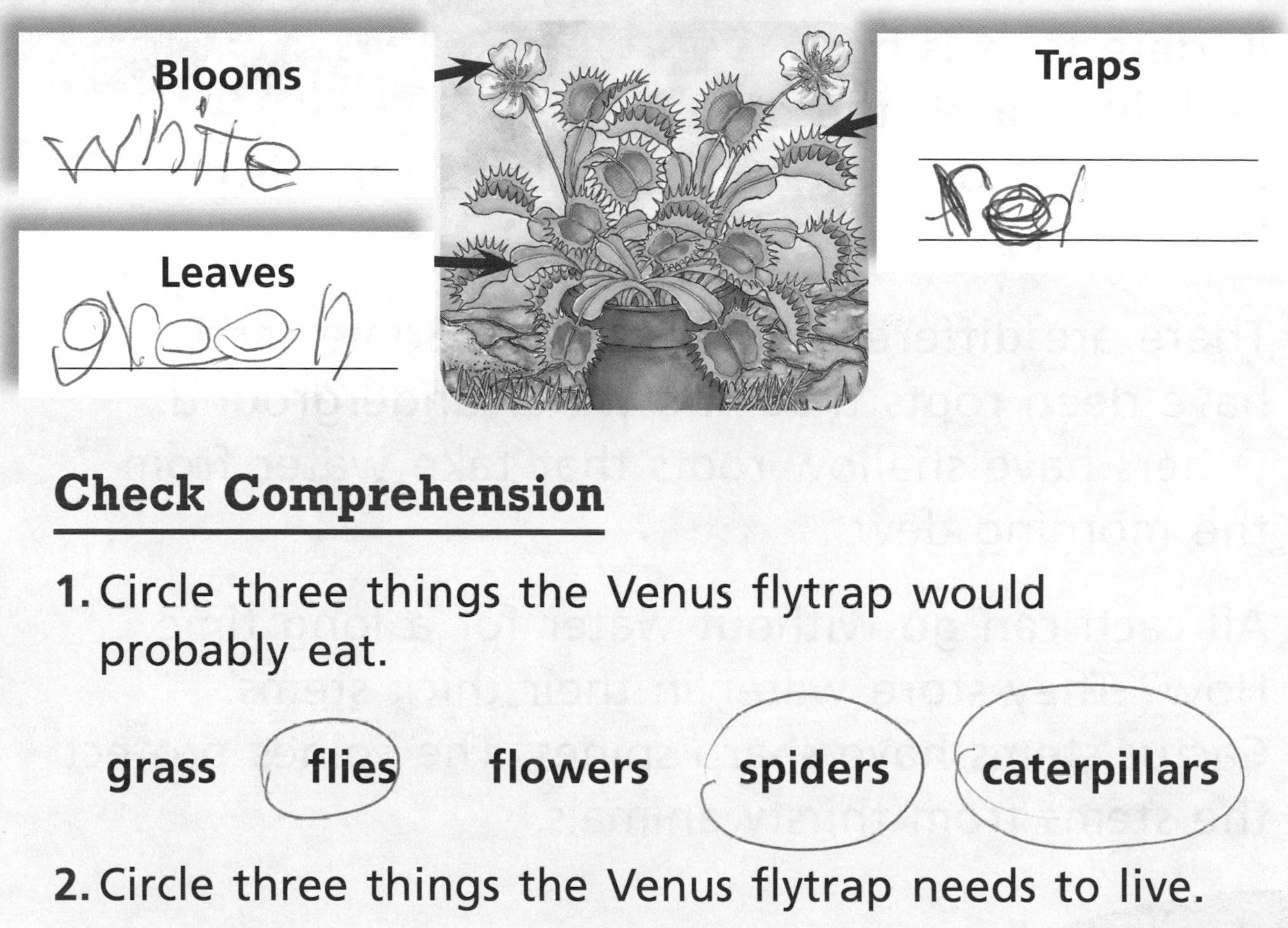

Check Comprehension

1. Circle three things the Venus flytrap would probably eat.

   grass flies flowers spiders caterpillars

2. Circle three things the Venus flytrap needs to live.

Vocabulary

When two words are put together they make a compound word, for example, "bedroom." Find a compound word on page 12 and one on page 13.

-
-

Cacti

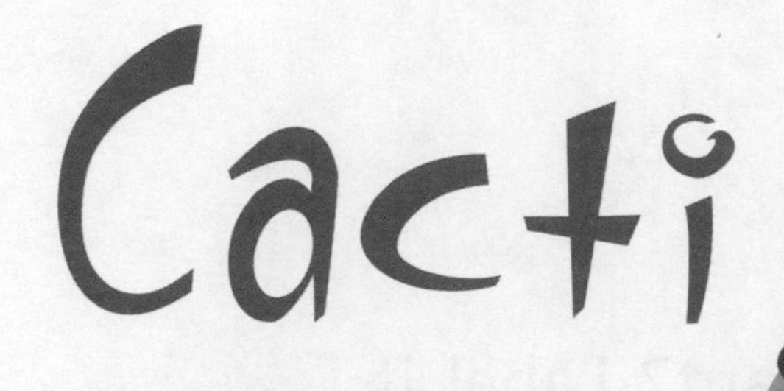

What is special about cacti?

In deserts, it is hot and dry during the day but very cold at night. Most plants can't live in this harsh land, but cacti can!

There are different kinds of cacti. Some cacti have deep roots that find water underground. Others have shallow roots that take water from the morning dew.

All cacti can go without water for a long time. How? They store water in their thick stems. Cactus stems have sharp spines. The spines protect the stems from thirsty animals.

Practice the Skill

Details about Cacti

Describe what each part of a cactus does.

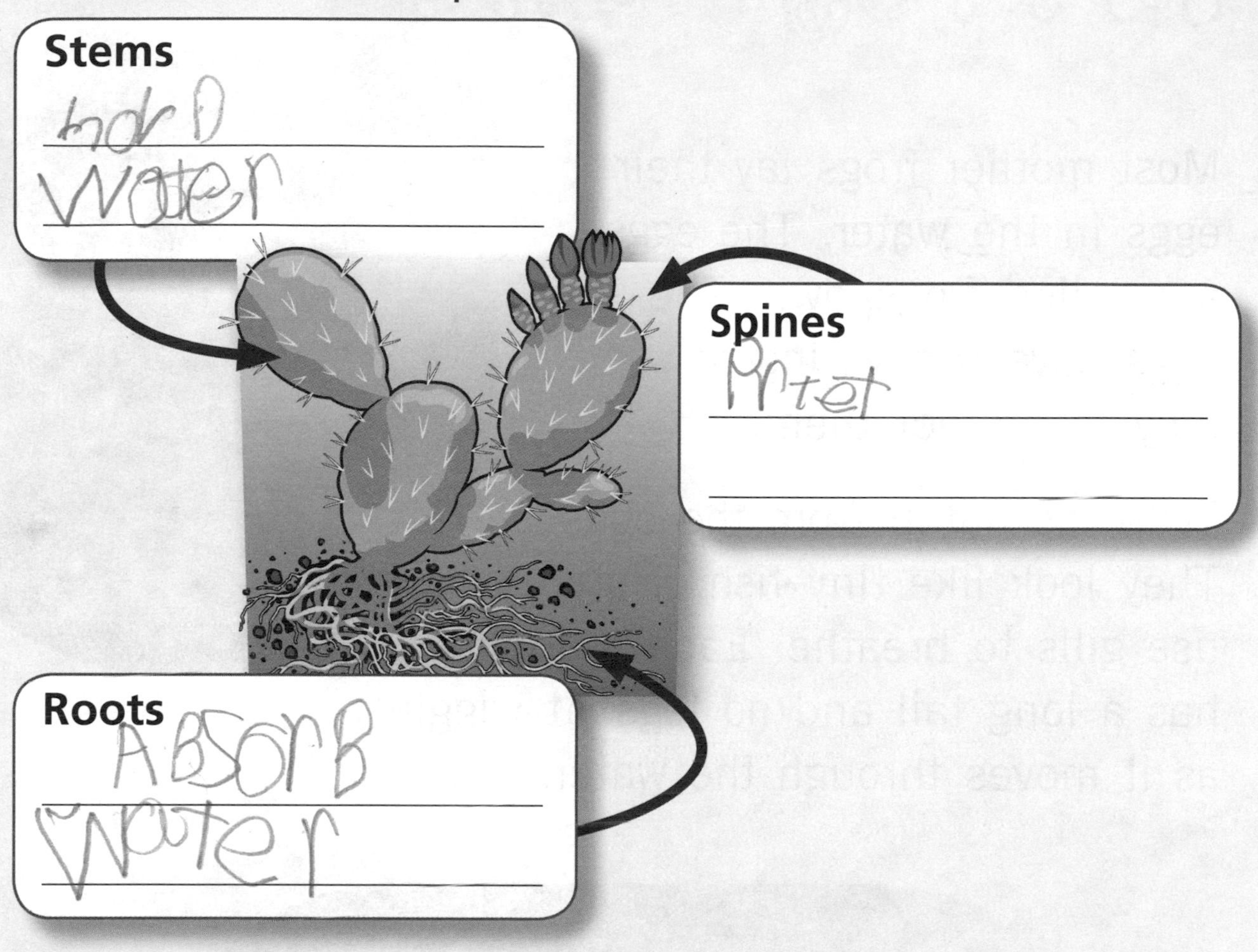

Check Comprehension

Why are cacti good desert plants?

They hold water.

Vocabulary

1/28/22

Find a word that means "more than one cactus."

Cacti

Sequencing Sequencing is putting things in the order they happened.

How does frogspawn turn into frogs?

Most mother frogs lay their eggs in the water. The eggs are called frogspawn. The eggs have a covering of jelly to protect them.

Tadpoles hatch from the eggs. They look like tiny fish. They use gills to breathe. Each tadpole has a long tail and no legs. It wiggles as it moves through the water.

Soon, each tadpole begins to grow hind legs. Then, its head flattens. Next, the tadpole's tail becomes shorter and its front legs grow. Finally, its gills and tail disappear.

Now, the frog needs to swim to the surface to gulp air into its lungs. It can leave the water and use its strong hind legs to hop on land.

Now it is a frog!

Practice the Skill

Sequence

1. Number the pictures in the correct order to show the frog's life cycle.

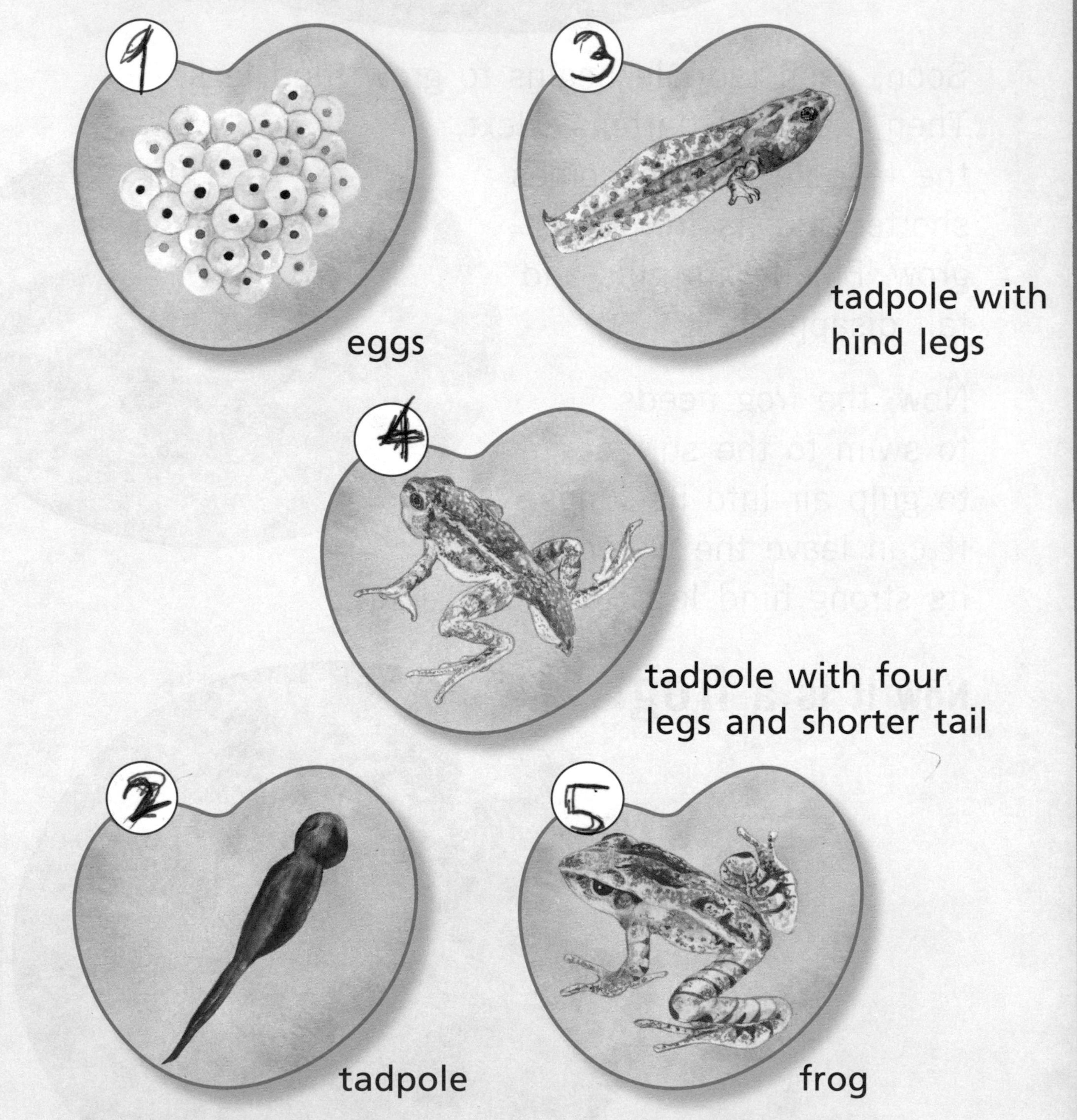

2. Number the boxes in order.

- ☐ Tadpoles grow front legs.
- ☐ Tadpoles use gills to breathe.
- ☐ Tadpoles use lungs to breathe.

Check Comprehension

1. Where do most mother frogs lay their eggs?

2. What happens to a tadpole's body just after it grows hind legs?

Vocabulary

- Find a word on page 18 that means the opposite of "big."
- Find a word on page 19 that means the opposite of "weak."

Look at Me Now!

How did Sabrina turn from an egg into a butterfly?

A little egg sat on a leaf. Slowly, a small, sleepy caterpillar crawled out. It was Sabrina. She was very hungry so she ate the shell of the egg.

Sabrina was still hungry so she munched on a leaf. She ate all the leaves around her. She got so large she had to grow a new skin and shed her old one. Sabrina ate and grew. She grew and shed.

At last, Sabrina had finished growing. She hung upside down from a leaf. She formed a chrysalis—a pouch sort of like a moth's cocoon. She looked like she was resting, but a lot was happening.

After two weeks, Sabrina was ready. She came out of her chrysalis and stretched.

"Look at that beautiful butterfly!" said a little boy.

Butterfly? wondered Sabrina. She glanced around. Sabrina saw that she had beautiful blue, red, and yellow wings. She spread her wings in the sunshine. Then she flew over and landed on a colorful flower.

I like being a butterfly! Sabrina thought to herself.

Practice the Skill

Sequence the Details

1. Write these details in order.

Sabrina ate a leaf. 2

Sabrina shed her skin. 3

Sabrina crawled out of an egg. 1

Sabrina formed a chrysalis. 4

1. ______________________________
2. ______________________________
3. ______________________________
4. ______________________________

2. Number each detail in order.

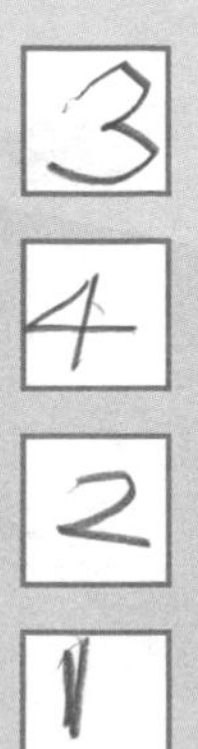

[3] Sabrina spread her wings.

[4] Sabrina flew to a flower.

[2] Sabrina glanced around.

[1] Sabrina stretched.

Check Comprehension

1. Why did Sabrina shed her old skin?

It was too small.

2. How long was Sabrina in the chrysalis?

She was in the chrysalis for two weeks.

3/4/22

As Busy as Beavers

What do kits do after they leave home?

Beavers are the largest rodents in North America. They have strong, sharp, long front teeth. Beavers work very hard to build their homes in the water. A beaver's home is called a *lodge*.

To build a lodge, beavers need deep water. First, they find some trees that grow next to a stream. Then, they use their strong teeth to gnaw at the tree trunks. The beavers gnaw and gnaw. The trees fall across the stream, making a dam.

Beavers eat pond weeds and other water plants.

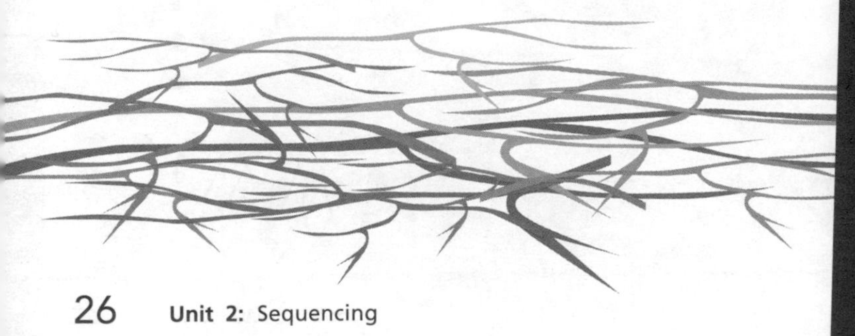

Next, beavers pack branches and twigs between the fallen trees. Then, the beavers use their tails to scoop up mud. They slap the mud onto the branches and twigs. The mud holds everything together. It stops the dam from floating away.

When the dam is finished, the beavers build their lodge. The lodge is also made from mud, branches, and sticks. The top part, where the beavers live, is warm and dry.

The beavers pack branches and twigs to make a dam.

After the lodge is built, the beavers have babies. These babies are called *kits*. When the kits are one year old, the beavers have more babies. This makes the lodge very crowded.

This beaver has three kits.

When the kits are two years old, they leave home. They build their own dams. They make their own lodges. Then they have their own families.

Beavers always work very hard. That is why people say that a hard worker is "as busy as a beaver."

Practice the Skill

Sequence the Steps

1. How do beavers build a dam? Number these steps in order.

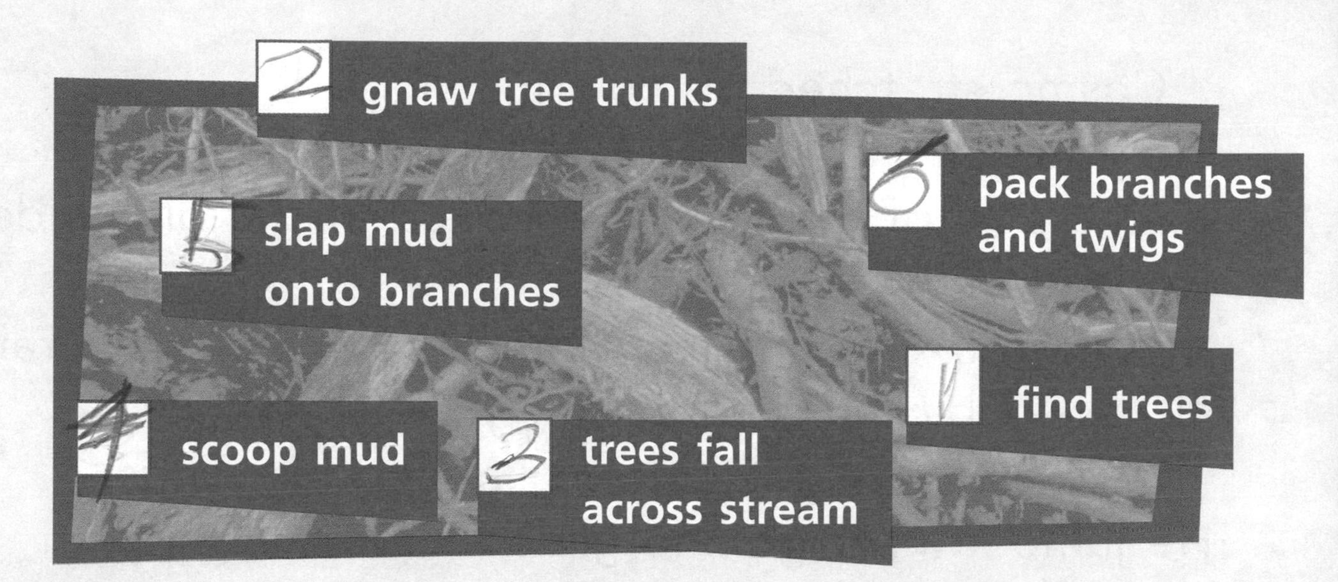

2. What happens after beaver families build a dam? Number these events in order.

 The lodge gets crowded.

 The two year olds build lodges.

Beavers have babies.

 The two year olds move out.

Vocabulary

What are beavers' babies called?

KITS

Fly with Me!

What was Cosmo going to do after he learned to fly?

Cosmo stretched his colorful wings. They felt strong and powerful. He hopped to the side of the nest and looked at the big, wide world below.

"Come to me!" called Mother from the next branch. "I have a big, juicy insect for you!"

With all his might, Cosmo flapped his wings. He jumped up high and glided smoothly through the air to his mother. He landed safely on the branch.

"Wonderful!" chirped Mother. "Soon you will catch your own supper."

And that's just what Cosmo began to do. Yum!

Practice the Skill

Sequence the Story Events

Write these story events in order.

Cosmo landed on the branch.	Cosmo's mother had an insect.
Cosmo stretched his wings.	Cosmo glided smoothly.

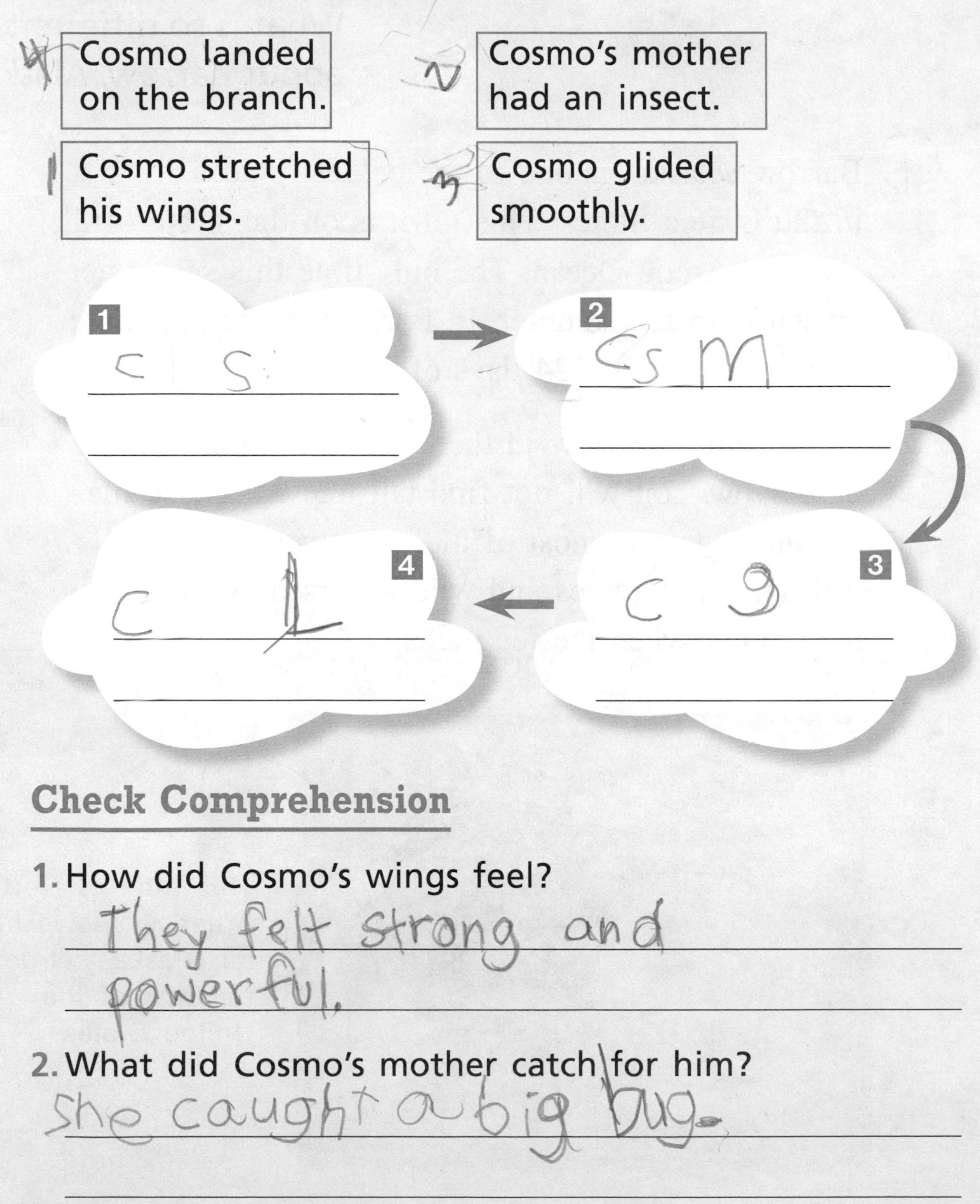

Check Comprehension

1. How did Cosmo's wings feel?

They felt strong and powerful.

2. What did Cosmo's mother catch for him?

She caught a big bug.

Main Idea The main ideas are the most important ideas in a text.

That's Cold!

What is so different about Barrow, Alaska?

Barrow, Alaska, is one of the coldest places in the United States. This town is on the shore of the icy cold Arctic Ocean. The only time this sea is not frozen is in the summer. In Barrow, the temperature is below freezing 324 days of the year!

Few plants can grow in the cold, Arctic climate of Barrow. You will not find tall trees, because the ground is frozen most of the year. In winter, very little grows. Grasses and wildflowers only grow in summer when the ice melts.

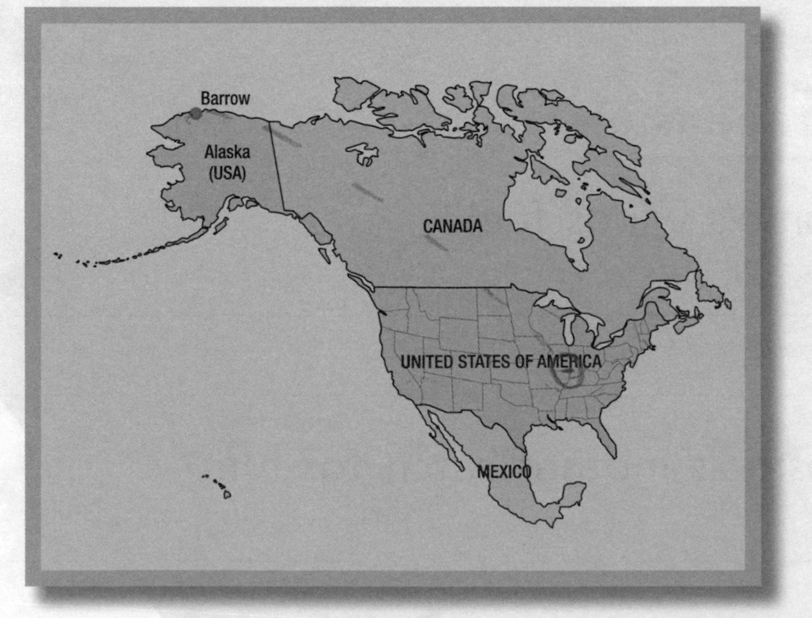

This map of North America shows how far Alaska is from the rest of the United States.

Day and night are different in Barrow than they are in most other places. Can you imagine days with no sunlight? For nine weeks of each year, the sun doesn't rise in Barrow. It is dark even in the daytime.

For another twelve weeks, between May and early August, the sun doesn't set. There is daylight all day and all night. That is why some people call this part of the world the "Land of the Midnight Sun."

During winter in Barrow, the ground and the sea are frozen.

Practice the Skill

Main Ideas

Write each main idea in the correct box to show which paragraph it comes from. The first one has been done for you.

1 • Barrow, Alaska, is one of the coldest places in the U.S.
3 • Day and night are different in Barrow.
2 • Few plants can grow in the cold Arctic climate.
4 • For twelve weeks, the sun doesn't set.
does not

1

Barrow, Alaska, is one of the coldest places in the U.S.

2

Few Plants can grow.

3

Day and night are different

4

For twelve weeks, the sun doesn't set

Sort Details

Write the details under the correct heading.

W • very little grows
S • grass grows
S • light day and night
S • sea not frozen
W • dark in daytime
S • ice melts

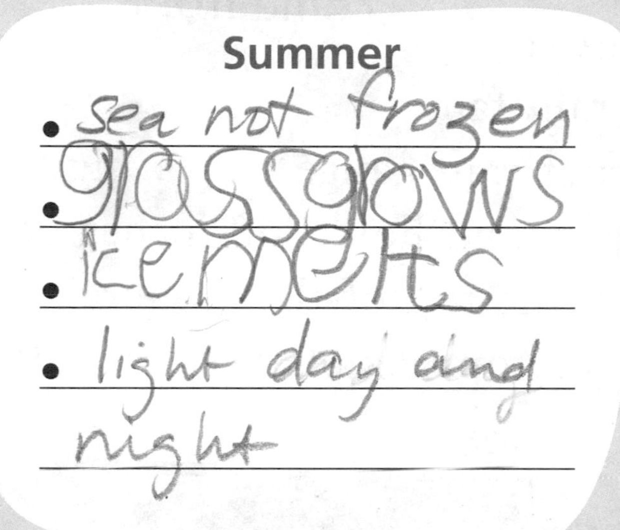

Winter

- very little grows
- dark in daytime
-
-

Vocabulary

Write two words from the text that mean "cold."

- frozen
- icy

Wet Mount Waialeale

Mount Waialeale, in Hawaii, is one of the wettest places in the world. This mountain is on the island of Kauai. The mountain can get 460 inches of rain each year!

Where does the power for the "tipping bucket" gauge come from?

People who measure rain use a gauge to check how much rain falls on Mount Waialeale. The first rain gauge was a big metal cylinder. It could collect and hold 900 inches of rain. The rain gauge was on the top of the mountain. It was very hard to get to the top. People used to ride up on mules, once a year.

The first rain gauge on Mount Waialeale

Mount Waialeale

Now, people who measure rain take a helicopter to the top of the mountain. The weather must be clear and calm for the helicopter to land there. Then, the gauge can be checked.

The type of gauge has changed, too. The gauge has a "tipping bucket" to collect the rainwater. It tips to one side to let the water run out. Then more rain collects. A switch counts the number of times the bucket tips. The counting switch runs on the power the gauge gets from the sun.

The way of measuring the rain has changed. However, the wet weather at Mount Waialeale has stayed the same!

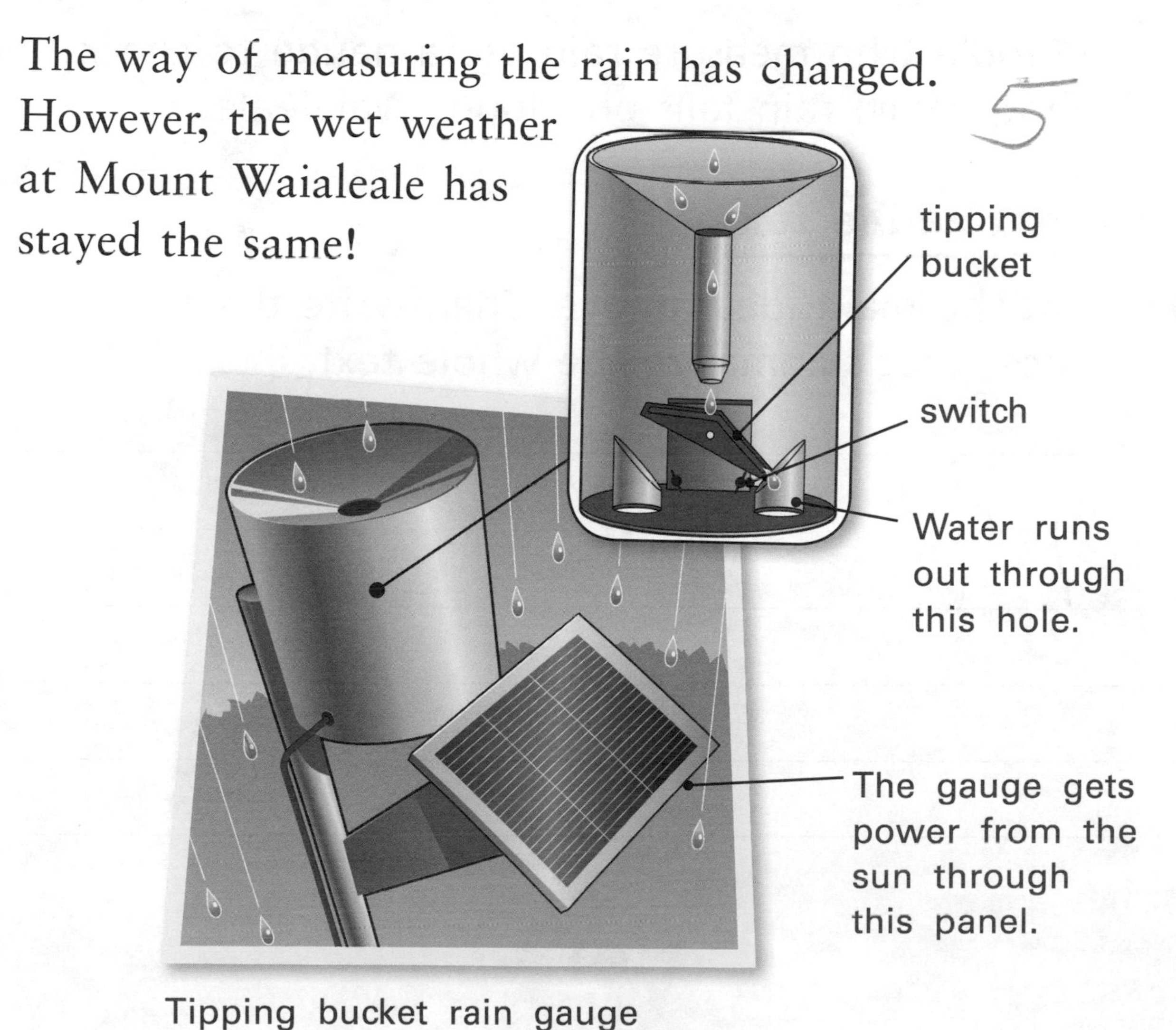

Tipping bucket rain gauge

Practice the Skill

Main Ideas

Number each of the following main ideas to show which paragraph it belongs to.

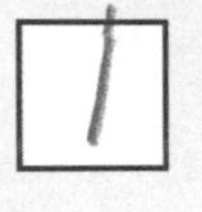

Mount Waialeale, in Hawaii, is one of the wettest places in the world.

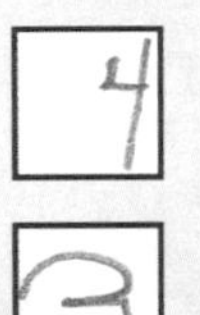

The type of gauge has changed, too.

Now, people who measure rain take a helicopter to the top of the mountain.

People who measure rain use a gauge to check how much rain falls on Mount Waialeale.

Summarize the Text

Look at the main ideas above. Then write the two sentences that summarize the whole text.

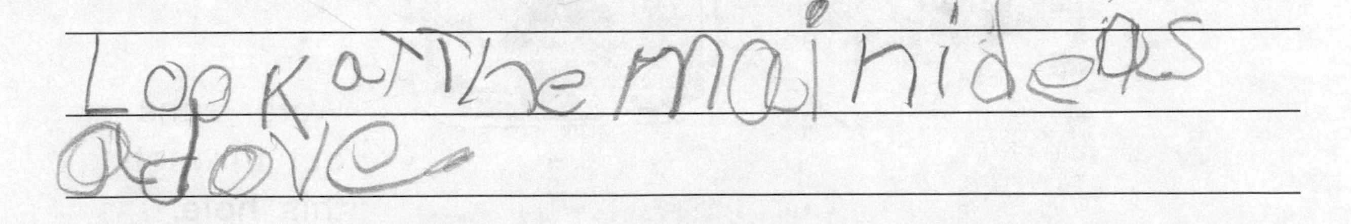

Identify Details

Check three details about measuring the rainwater.

- [2] Rain collects in a bucket.
- [1] A bucket tips water out.
- [4] It is the wettest place in the world.
- [5] It is hard to get to the top.
- [3] A switch counts the number of tips.

Check Comprehension

How many times a year did people ride mules to the top of the mountain?

Once a year.

Vocabulary

- What is a rain gauge?

  It collects water.

- *Gauge* is not pronounced the way it looks. Write two words that rhyme with "gauge."

  - Sage
  - age

Rocky the Mountain Goat

What were the strange new animals that Rocky saw?

Rocky the mountain goat lived on Mount Rainier. Mount Rainier is a very tall mountain in Washington. It is always very cold on Mount Rainier, but Rocky didn't mind.

Rocky's thick, white coat kept him warm and safe. His white fur made it hard to see him against the white snow. This helped protect him from some of the other animals that lived on the mountain. Bobcats, mountain lions, and bears were Rocky's enemies. He was friends with the beavers, bats, and chipmunks.

Rocky was a very happy mountain goat. He enjoyed romping through snow and climbing over rocks on his special hooves. He snacked on heather and other small plants that grew between the rocks.

One day, Rocky saw strange animals he had never seen before. They were climbing up the mountain. The new animals didn't have fur to protect them. Their coats were brightly colored. They walked on two legs with big feet, but they had two other limbs. They used these limbs to help them climb over the rocks. The new animals had packs on their backs and made noises at each other as they climbed. Rocky froze. Are they dangerous? he wondered. What do you think?

Practice the Skill

Find the Main Idea

Number each paragraph in the text. Then number the following main ideas to show which paragraph each one belongs to.

 Rocky the mountain goat lived on Mount Rainier.

 One day, Rocky saw strange animals he had never seen before.

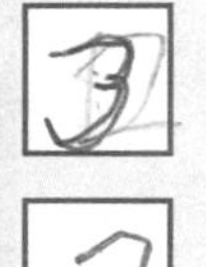 Rocky was a very happy mountain goat.

2 Rocky's thick, white coat kept him warm and safe.

Summarize the Text

Write the two sentences that summarize the whole text.

- Rocky did not know if the strange animals were dangerous.
- Rocky lived on Mount Rainier.
- One day, Rocky saw animals he had never seen before.
- His coat kept him warm and safe.

Rocky lived on the Mount.

His coat kept

4/21/22

The Ocean Depths

What is so unusual about the deep trenches?

The ocean floor is not flat, as you might think. It has many deep trenches. Many of these deep trenches have been made by powerful earthquakes.

The deepest trench is over 36,000 feet deep. It is near the island of Guam in the Pacific Ocean. The tallest mountain in the world would not fill up this trench!

No plants can live in this deep part of the ocean. This is because there's no sunlight. All plants need sunlight.

Animals can live on the ocean floor. Some of these animals are shrimps, sea worms, and sea cucumbers. Scientists are working to learn how these animals can live in the deep, dark ocean.

This sea cucumber lives on a sea sponge.

Practice the Skill

Main Idea

Number each paragraph in the text. Then number the following main ideas to show which paragraph each one belongs to.

☐ No plants can live in this deep part of the ocean.

☐ Animals can live on the ocean floor.

☐ The ocean floor is not flat.

☐ The deepest trench is over 36,000 feet deep.

Summarize the Text

Read each sentence below. Which one is the main idea of the text? Circle it.

There is no sunlight in the trenches.

The ocean floor has many deep trenches.

Animals can live on the ocean floor.

Compare and Contrast To compare and contrast, find what is the same and what is different.

At the Fair

What different games did Mario and Grandpa play?

Mario had always wanted to go to a fair. One day, a fair came to town, so Grandpa took him.

When they arrived at the fair, Grandpa said, "When I was young, we didn't have a Slippery Dippery. We had donkey rides instead. But we did have a Ferris wheel."

"I want to go on the Slippery Dippery first!" said Mario.

Whoosh!

"I feel a bit dizzy," he said when he got off.

"I'll go next!" said Grandpa.

Whoosh!

"I feel a bit wobbly," Grandpa said.

"Maybe a ride on the Ferris wheel will make us feel better," said Mario.

After the Ferris wheel, Grandpa and Mario ate ice cream. Then, Grandpa said, "Now I'm going to play Knock the Coconuts!" He knocked three coconuts off the platform. "I'm a great pitcher!" Grandpa said proudly. He won a huge, cuddly lion.

Next, Mario played Baskets. He got four balls through the hoop and into the basket. "I'm a great basketball player!" Mario said proudly. He won a huge, cuddly panda bear.

"Do you want to come back next year?" asked Grandpa.

"Yes, please!" said Mario.

Practice the Skill

Same and Different

Fill in the answers about Grandpa and Mario at the fair. Then write "S" for same or "D" for different in the third column.

	Grandpa	Mario	S or D
What did they ride first?		✓	S
How did they feel after the first ride?	slippery dippery	✓	S
What did they ride next?	Ferris wheel		S
What did they eat?	ice cream		S
What games did they play?	Knockdown	basketball	D
What did they win?	lion	panda bear	D

Map the Sequence

Draw a map to show what Grandpa and Mario did at the fair. Label the map and number the labels in sequence.

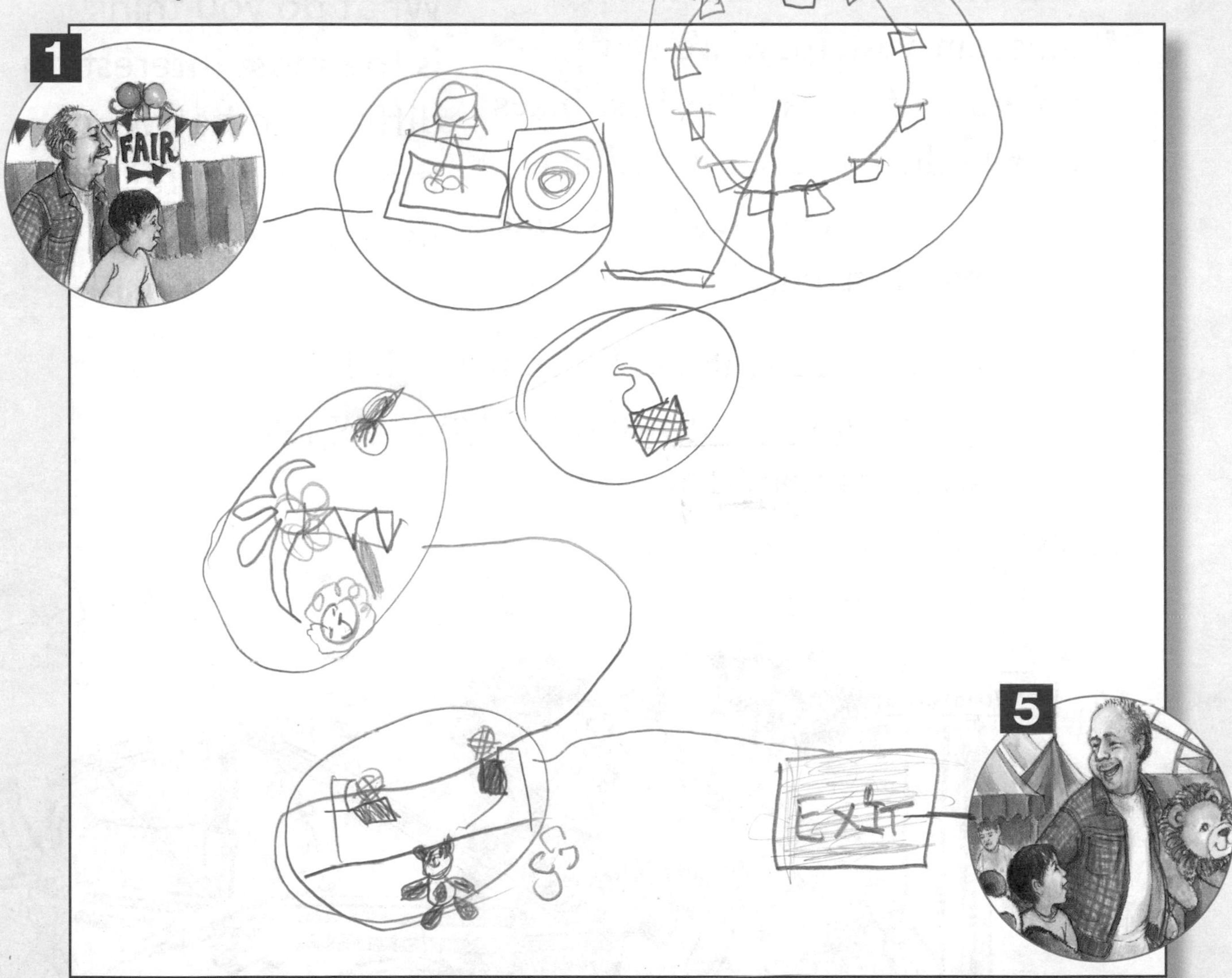

Vocabulary

Find a word on page 47 that means "later on." Then find one that means "very big."

- ______________________
- ______________________

The Weirdest Bike Ever!

Our class went to the history museum yesterday. We saw a model of one of the first bikes ever built. It was all wood and did not have any metal. My bike has lots of metal.

What do you think is the most interesting difference between the old bike and the new bike?

It had two wheels, the same as mine. It had spokes, like mine, but it did not have any pedals! How weird is that? The riders had to put their feet on the ground and scoot themselves along.

The seat of the old bike wasn't soft like mine. It was wooden. Ouch! The old bike didn't have any brakes like bikes have now. The riders had to stop moving by dragging their feet along the ground. I bet that hurt going down hills!

The old bike couldn't turn because the handlebars weren't attached to the wheel. It looked more like a rocking horse than a real bike. I'm glad I have my bike to ride!

Practice the Skill

Same and Different

1. Fill in the diagram to show how the first bike and a new bike are the same and different.

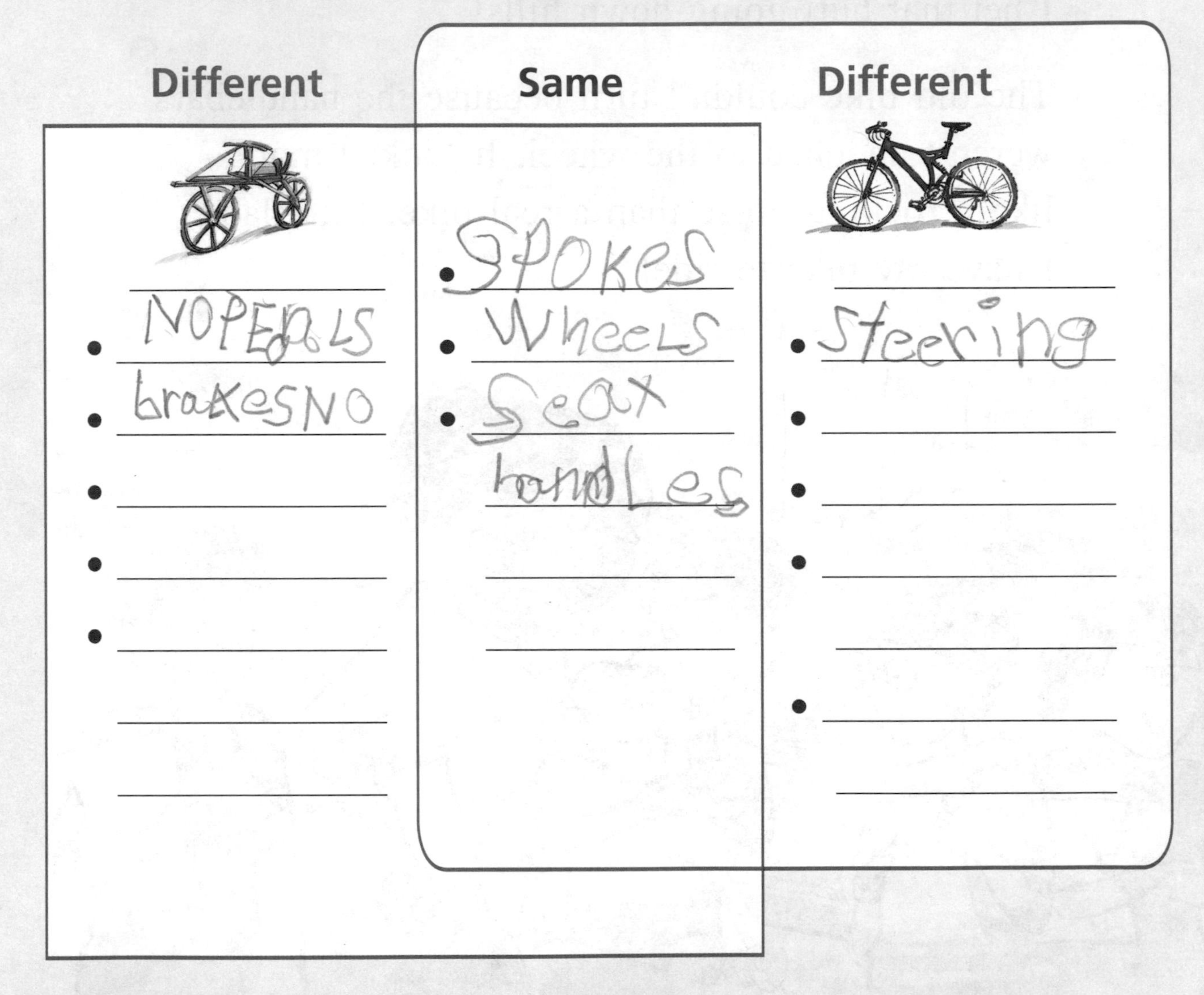

2. List three things new bikes have that the old bike did not have.

- good Seats.
- PEdaLS.
- Bags.

Check Comprehension

1. What do you think is the best thing about new bikes?

I think the best thing is there are brakes.

2. What do you think is the worst thing about the old bike?

The worst thing is dragging your feet.

3. Which bike do you think is safer to ride? Why?

The new because it has brakes.

Writing

If you designed a bike, what would you like it to do?

Two Boys

What differences does the boy notice in the old photos?

Up in the attic, I found some photos in a dusty box. One photo shows a boy and his dad in a funny old car. They look a little like Dad and me, but our car is more modern than that (even though Dad drives a used station wagon).

There is a photo of the boy and his family eating a turkey dinner. They're having a good time, just like we do at big family meals. In another photo, they are washing the dishes. I'm glad we have a dishwasher.

There is also a photo of the boy going to school. His hat is sort of like my baseball cap, but his school bag is different from my backpack. He is taking the train to school. I take the electric subway train, and I bet it goes much faster than that old steam train.

The boy and his dad are fishing in another picture. I like to go fishing with my dad, too. I guess my life is like this boy's life in many ways.

There's also a photo of the boy writing a letter at his desk, using a fountain pen and a bottle of ink. I wonder what he would think of today's pens. And, what would he think of e-mail?

It turns out I could ask him. I showed Great-Grandpa the pictures, and guess what? He said that boy is him. Wow! I guess the boy in the pictures really is a lot like me!

Practice the Skill

Compare and Contrast: Then and Now

1. Fill in the chart to show what is different from when the boy's great-grandpa was young and today.

	Great-Grandpa's Day	Today
cleaning dishes		
trains		
writing		

2. List three things that are the same about the writer and the boy in the pictures.

- ______________________________
- ______________________________
- ______________________________

Writing

What things do you have today that your great-grandparents didn't have when they were young?

Two Bedrooms

What was the biggest difference between the two rooms?

Now

My bedroom is white and my carpet is red.
Spaceships fly over the quilt on my bed.
My desk and computer are right by the door.
My books and my teddy bear sit on the floor.

Then

Gran's bedroom was yellow, her wood floor was bare.
Her desk had a pen and some ink and a chair.
Her books and her teddy bear sat on the shelf.
Her mother had sewn the blue quilt by herself.

Practice the Skill

Same and Different

Fill in the diagram to show how the two bedrooms are the same and how they are different.

Now		Then
Different	Same	Different

Check Comprehension

Who sewed Gran's blue quilt?

____

Vocabulary

Write two rhyming words from the text.

- ______________
- ______________

Drawing Conclusions/Predicting Outcomes Use information from a text to decide what might happen next.

Riddles

Which clues tell you what these things are?

What Am I?

I sit on the kitchen counter.
I have an electric plug.
I have a dial to set.
You put slices inside me.
They pop up when they are ready.

What Am I?

I have wheels because you need
to pull me all around the house.
When you turn me on, I make
a loud noise.

I suck the dirt from the floor.
I can even suck the dust bunnies
from under your bed!

Practice the Skill

Draw Conclusions

1. Read the riddle on page 60. What is it about?

    ____

2. Now read only the first two lines of the same riddle. What other things might these two lines describe?

    - ______________________________
    - ______________________________

3. Read the riddle on page 61. What is it about?

    ____

4. Write three details that helped you answer the riddle.

    - ______________________________
    - ______________________________
    - ______________________________

Predict Outcomes

1. What might happen if you turn the dial on a toaster all the way up?

2. What might happen if you turn the dial all the way down?

3. What do you think a pet cat or dog is likely to do when a vacuum cleaner is turned on?

4. If your vacuum cleaner does not work or you do not have one, what else could you use to clean your house?

Write a Riddle

Think of something in your house. Write three things about it and ask someone to guess what it is.

Don't Let the Bedbugs Bite

How do you know beds were less comfortable hundreds of years ago?

I love my bed! It has a box spring, which is thick and bouncy. The mattress is soft and bouncy, too. When I go to sleep, I love to snuggle into my bed.

When Mom and Dad kiss me goodnight, they say, "Night, night, sleep tight. Don't let the bedbugs bite." Do you know why they say that? I do.

Hundreds of years ago, beds didn't have box springs. They had frames with ropes woven across them. Slowly the ropes would sag. They had to be tightened up again.

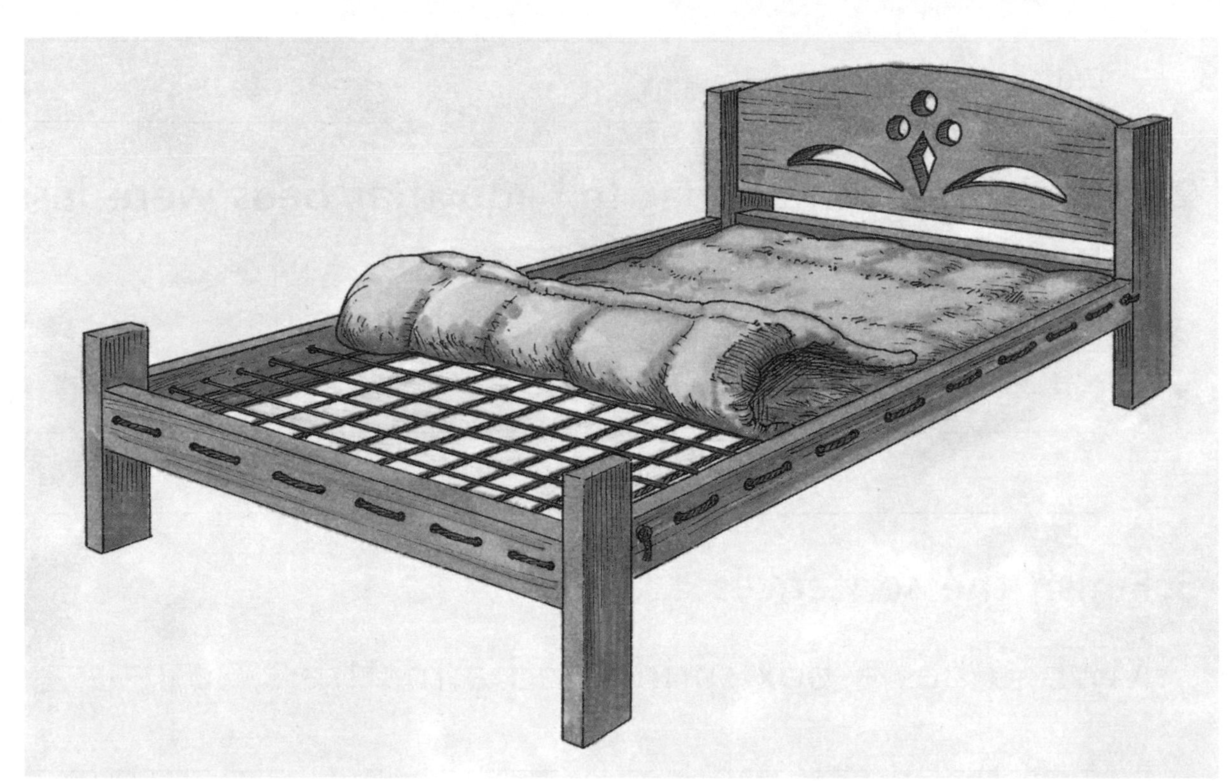

This rope-frame bed has a straw-filled mattress.

A thin mattress was put on top of the ropes. The mattresses were cloth bags filled with straw. After a while, the bags got very lumpy. They got damp, too, because the houses were cold and damp.

Sometimes, bugs lived in the straw. The bugs would bite people while they were asleep. They left bumps like mosquito bites.

Practice the Skill

Draw Conclusions

1. Write two things that tell you the writer's bed is comfortable.
   - ______________________
   - ______________________
2. Write three things that tell you that beds were less comfortable hundreds of years ago.
   - ______________________
   - ______________________
   - ______________________
3. Finish the sentences.

   My bed has a box spring and a mattress, so it is

   ______________________.

   The lumpy straw mattress was ____________

   ______________________.

   During the night, the bugs in the straw mattresses

   ______________________.

   When the bedbugs bit people, they left lumps like

   ______________________.

Predict Outcomes

1. When people were bitten by bedbugs, how do you think they felt in the morning?

____

2. Write two things you could do that would make a lumpy straw mattress more comfortable.

- ____
- ____

Same and Different

Write "T" for true or "F" for false in each box.

	Mattresses Then	Mattresses Now
comfortable		
damp		
soft and bouncy		
made of straw		

Vocabulary

Find the words for what goes below a mattress.

____

Clocks

Clocks come in all shapes, sizes, colors, and styles. Some clocks are big and heavy and take up a lot of space. Some are so small they can fit on your wrist. Clocks have been around for hundreds of years, but they have changed a lot.

How do you know the old clocks didn't always work well?

Long ago, there was only one kind of clock. It was called a sundial. People saw how the shadow on the sundial moved during the day. It worked quite well, but there were times when a sundial was no help at all.

Next, people used candles to tell the time. They marked a candle with lines and the wax melted down from line to line as it burned. Using candles didn't always work, either.

Later on, the hourglass was invented. The glass had a special tube shape. Sand flowed from the top of the tube to the bottom in one hour. The hourglass had to be turned over every hour so the sand could flow back again. But if the glass tube got blocked, things went wrong.

Mechanical clocks were invented after that. They used pendulums and springs that turned little wheels. The wheels moved the clock's hands. Mechanical clocks worked well.

Today, many people use electronic clocks. These modern clocks can tell the time very well.

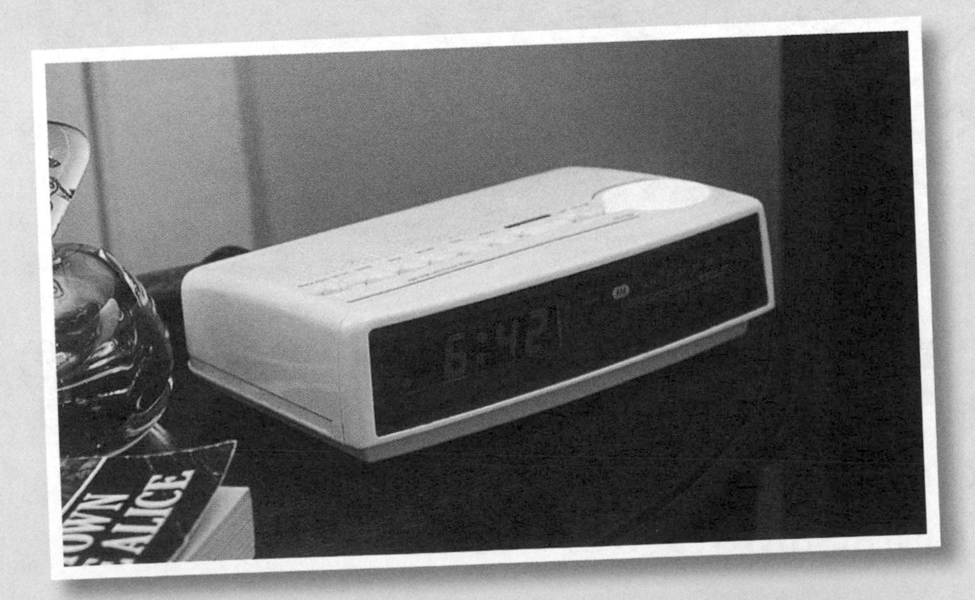

Practice the Skill

Draw Conclusions

1. With a sundial, people told the time by looking at the ________________.

A sundial didn't always work because

____

____.

2. With a candle, people told the time by

______________________________.

A candle didn't always work because

____

____.

3. Mechanical clocks worked well because they had

____

____.

Check Comprehension

Which clock tells the best time? ________________

Writing

If you didn't have a modern clock to tell time, which clock would you like to use? Why?

The Musicians

What did the children use to make music?

Nina was three years old. She wanted to make some noise. Mom gave her a pot and a wooden spoon to hit it with.

The older kids thought this was a great idea! Lola got a cardboard box with a lid, and tapped it with chopsticks. Her drum went thump, thump. Luca put some seeds in a tin can with a lid. His seeds went swish, swish.

Now they could make music! "It's a lovely day," said Mom. "Why don't you play your music outside?" Off they went, happily making music together.

Practice the Skill

Draw Conclusions

1. Finish the sentences.

   Nina hit a pot with a spoon.

   She made a ______________________________.

   Luca shook a tin can with seeds in it.

   He made a ______________________________.

2. Why do you think their mom wanted them to play their music outside?

   ____

   ____

Check Comprehension

1. What was the name of the youngest child?

   ____

2. Who thought making noise was a great idea?

   ____

3. What did Lola use to make her drum?

   ____

Fact and Opinion A fact is information that is true, and an opinion is what someone thinks or believes.

Ask the Pet Vet

Do you think a goldfish or a dog is a better pet for Charlie?

To petvet@VetHelpline.com
From charlie_r@kwikmail.com
Sent January 14, 2006
Subject Pet advice

Dear Pet Vet,

I really want a pet. My parents say I can get one if I learn how to take care of it. They think pets can be a lot of work.

We don't have a big yard. I also play soccer and have to practice my tuba after school. My room is pretty small. What do you think would be the best pet for me?

Thank you,

Charlie

To charlie_r@kwikmail.com
From petvet@VetHelpline.com
Sent January 14, 2006
Subject RE: Pet advice

Dear Charlie,

All pets need:

- food
- water
- a clean, safe place to live and sleep

Some pets also need:

- exercise
- grooming and bathing
- special homes
- training

One great idea for a fun and easy pet is a goldfish. I think goldfish are beautiful and smart, and they are the best pets for busy people. This will be a great first pet for you! All they need are a clean tank, food, and some attention. Good luck with your new pet!

Best wishes,

Pet Vet

Practice the Skill

Fact and Opinion

1. Write "F" for fact or "O" for opinion in each box.

- I think goldfish are smart. ☐
- Some pets need exercise. ☐
- Goldfish need a clean tank. ☐
- Goldfish are the best pets for busy people. ☐

2. What facts did Charlie tell the vet so the vet could think of a good pet for him?

____

____

____

3. List three important facts about caring for pets.

- ____
- ____
- ____

4. Finish the sentences.

I think a goldfish would be a good pet for Charlie because ____

____.

I think a lamb would not be a good pet for Charlie because ____

____.

Vocabulary

- Find a word on page 74 that means the opposite of "big."

____

- Find a word on page 75 that means the opposite of "dirty."

____

Writing

Sally lives in the country. She has a big back yard. She likes to go for long walks with her mom. What would be a good pet for her? Why?

Best Pet

Do you think the judge chose the best pet in the show?

Every year, I go with my family to the Luckyville Town Fair. This year I entered my chameleon Dakota in the "Best Pet" show. I hoped he would win a prize!

Waiting for the judge was scary. I thought that if I crossed my fingers, toes, and legs, it would bring me good luck. I tried to cross my eyes, too, but then I couldn't see. The judge looked around at all of the pets.

A parrot said, "Hello, Friend!"

"I bet he's a noisy pet," said the judge.

A dog rolled over and begged.

"I think that's one clever dog!" said the judge.

"Well, young man," the judge said to me. "What can your chameleon do?"

"Watch this!" I answered. Dakota ran up my arm and sat on my head. Then his green skin turned the same color brown as my hair.

"Now, that's an amazing trick!" said the judge. Then she looked at my crossed fingers, toes, and legs. "And I think you do good tricks, too," she laughed.

Who won the prize?

Dakota!

Practice the Skill

Fact and Opinion

1. Write the sentences in the correct column.

- A dog rolled over.
- I think that dog's clever.
- I bet he's a noisy pet.
- A bird talked.
- That's an amazing trick.
- The lizard turned brown.

Fact	Opinion

2. What could each of these animals do?

parrot ______________________________

____

dog ______________________________

____

chameleon ______________________________

____

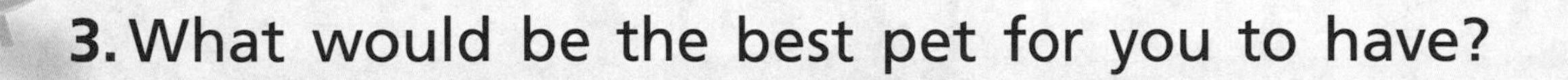

3. What would be the best pet for you to have?

____

4. Write two facts and two opinions about the pet you have chosen.

Facts

____

____

Opinions

____

____

Draw Conclusions

Chameleons can change their skin color to the color of what they are lying on. Why do you think they do that?

____

____

____

____

____

An Owner for Percy

Why do you think the puppy is the best pet for the little girl?

Percy the puppy jumped up and down in the corner of the pet shop window. His brother was stretching and his sister was curled up, sleeping quietly. The goldfish swam silently around their aquarium. Even the cockatoo didn't have much to say.

Percy thought life in the pet shop window was too quiet. He wanted to run around. The mice in the first window were running. They chased each other in the wheel inside their house. Now that's more like it, thought Percy as he watched the mice. Everyone else seems happy being quiet. Everyone but me!

The next day, Percy saw a little girl watching him. She sat in a chair with big wheels. Percy ran to the front of the window and jumped up and down.

"Look, Daddy!" said the girl. "I think that brown puppy is so cute. Look how he's jumping and wagging his tail. He can't wait to come out and meet me. I think that's the kind of puppy I want, a puppy who will jump up on my lap."

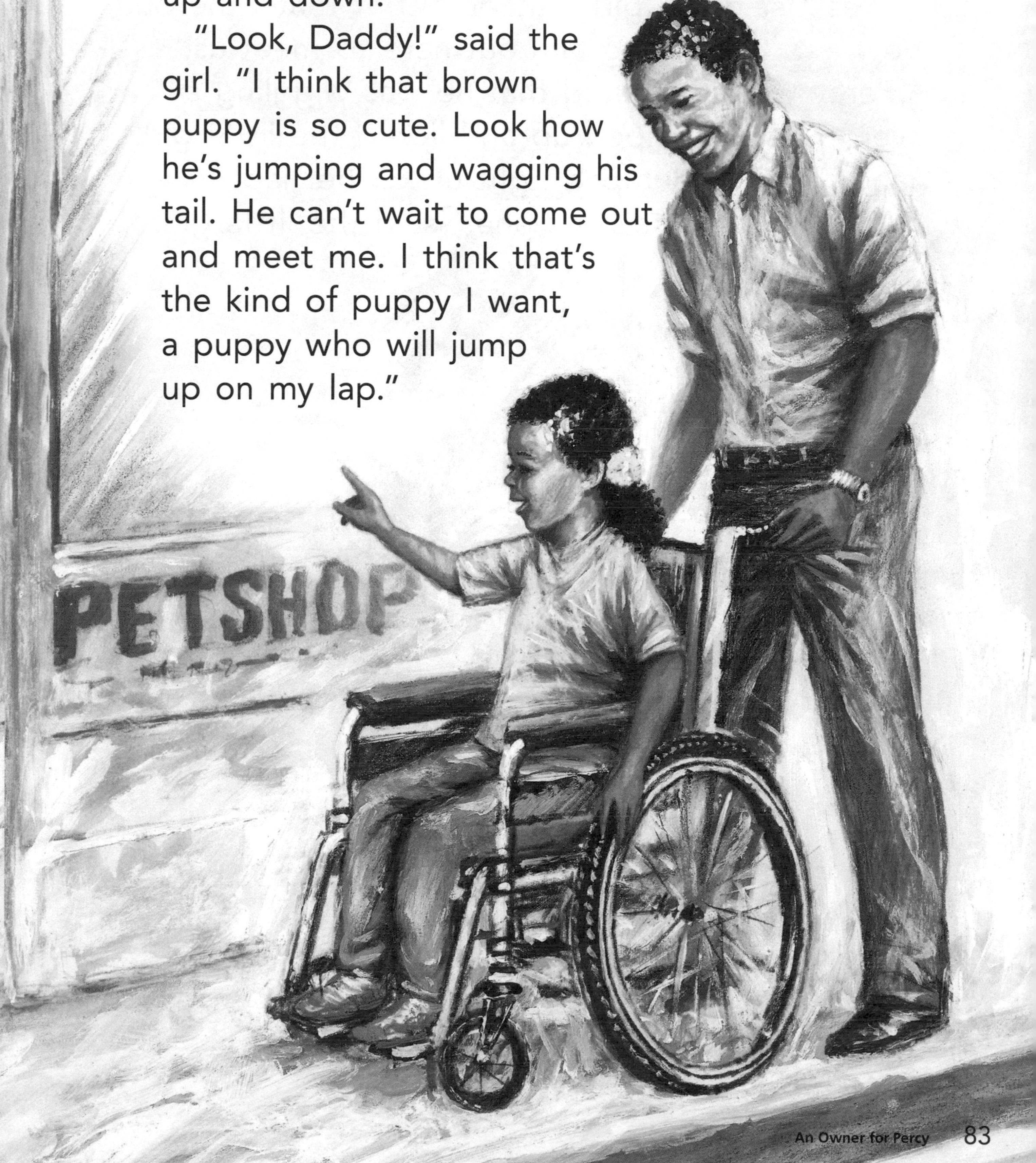

Percy suddenly felt happy. He put his paw up on the glass to say hello.

"Yes!" said the girl's father. "I bet that's the one we want. Let's bring him out here to meet us!"

Percy was so excited that he was wiggling all over. First he jumped up and licked the little girl's hand. Then he jumped right up on her lap!

"Now I know he's the one," said the little girl.

Practice the Skill

Fact and Opinion

1. Write "F" for fact or "O" for opinion in each box.

- Percy jumped up and down. ☐
- Percy thought it was too quiet. ☐
- Percy licked the little girl's hand. ☐
- "I bet that's the one we want." ☐
- Percy had a brother and a sister. ☐

Check Comprehension

1. Why didn't Percy like the pet shop?

____

____

____

2. Why did the little girl choose Percy?

____

____

____

My Mouse

I have a tiny, active pet
Who needs a special house.
He has a tail and whiskers, too.
He's my furry friend named Mouse.

Damon says, "I bet he smells!"
Mae thinks he's such a bore.
But Mouse is sweet and frisky,
And I couldn't love him more!

Do you agree that mice are the best pets?

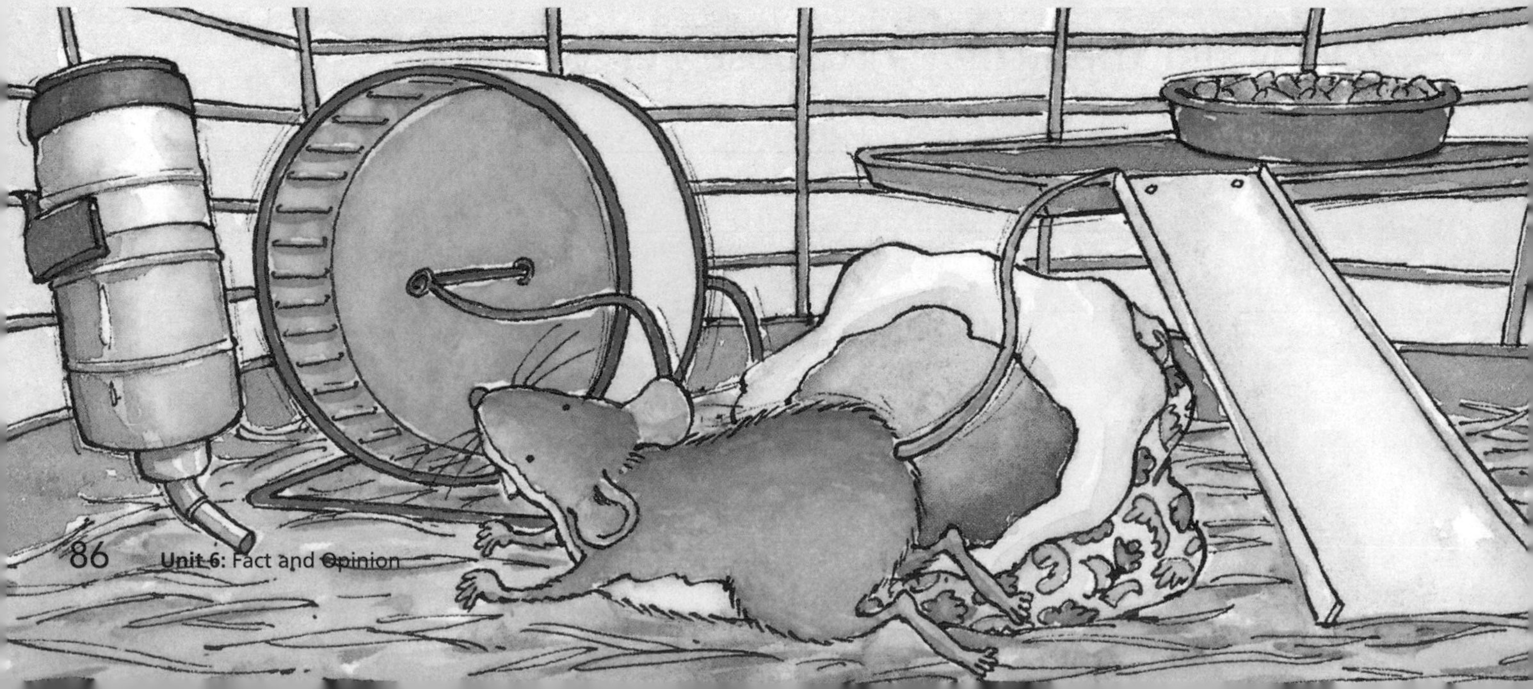

Mouse is always cleaning,
Or running 'round his wheel.
He likes to gnaw, and loves to chew
And nibble through each meal!

I love watching Mouse at play
Or sleeping in his nest.
My friends think mice are silly pets
But I think they're the best.

Practice the Skill

Fact and Opinion

Write "F" for fact or "O" for opinion in each box.

- Mouse has a tail and whiskers. ☐
- My friends think mice are silly pets. ☐

Mouse Facts

Write some facts about Mouse.

Different Opinions

What did each person think about Mouse?

- Damon ____________________
- Mae ____________________
- Mouse's owner ____________________

Acknowledgments

Illustrations
Elizabeth Bastian, p. 20; Peter Campbell, pp. 40–41, 42; Neil Curtis, pp. 2, 22, 23 (butterfly); Rae Dale, pp. 78–79, 80, 81; Ian Forss, pp. 12–13, 14, 15, 86, 87; Marjory Gardner, p. 30; Trish Hill, p. 50–51, 52; Andrea Jaretzki, p. 23 (flower); Julie Knoblock, pp. 60, 61, 62, 63; Naomi Lewis, pp. 46–47, 49; Richard Mordern, pp. 17, 36, 37, 39; Xiangyi Mo, p. 65; Dimitrios Prokopis, pp. 4, 6, 32; Pat Reynolds, p. 72; Chantal Stewart, pp. 54, 55, 56; Rachel Tonkin, p. 58; Mark Wilson, pp. 82–83, 84.

Photographs
AFP Photo DPP/Henning Kaiser, p. 9; Amphibian Research Centre/frogs.org.au/Lydia Fucsko, pp. 18, 21 (bottom); APL/Pawel Libera, pp. 8, 10, /Jose Luis Pelaez, Inc., p. 64, /Galen Rowell, p. 33, /Michael T. Sedam, p. 36; Auscape International, pp. 26, 27, 29; Bruce Coleman, Inc., p. 69; Malcolm Cross, p. 70 (bottom); Lindsay Edwards Photography, p. 68 (right); Pavel German/antphoto.com, p. 19 (bottom); Lonely Planet Images/Tim Rock, p. 44; Photodisc, pp. 68 (left and middle), 70 (top), 74, 75, 76, 77; photolibrary.com, pp. 16, 28; Chris & Sandra Pollitt/antphoto.com, pp. 19 (top and middle), 21 (top); Royalty Free/Corbis, cover; United States Department of Agriculture, p. 5.